This book is dedicated to the spirit of the Ethiopian wolf

A TEMPLAR BOOK

First published in the UK in 1997 by Templar Publishing, an imprint of The Templar Company plc.

Distributed in the UK by Ragged Bears Ltd, Ragged Appleshaw, Andover, Hampshire SP11 9HX.

Devised and produced by The Templar Company plc, Pippbrook Mill, London Road, Dorking, Surrey RH4 1JE, in association with The Born Free Foundation.

Edited by Mike Janulewicz. Designed by Mike Jolley.

This book has been printed and bound by Proost N.V. in Belgium using 100% recycled paper.

No dioxin-producing chlorine is used in the manufacturing process.

ISBN 1-898784-71-X

the Wolf Watchers

WRITTEN BY *Alison Hood &*
Claudio Sillero-Zubiri

ILLUSTRATED BY *Andy DaVolls*

TEMPLAR
PUBLISHING

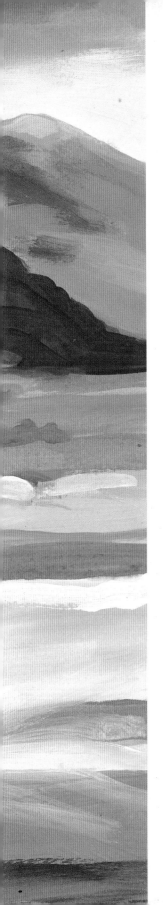

With less than 400 individuals remaining, the Ethiopian wolf could be the next of the Earth's large mammals to become extinct. Threatened by loss of its habitat, persecution and, most lethal of all, the spread of disease carried by domestic dogs, this beautiful creature could disappear altogether by the turn of the century.

If we are to save this rare and intelligent species, we need to act now - by ensuring a safe haven for the wolves that still remain, by creating a better understanding of these creatures among the people of Ethiopia and, most importantly, through the introduction of a vaccination programme to combat killer diseases. On the following pages you can read the story of one wolf pack saved, at least for the moment, from the threat of rabies. There are many others to follow. If we can help them too, we may just succeed in bringing the Ethiopian wolf back from the brink of extinction.

DR CLAUDIO SILLERO-ZUBIRI, I.U.C.N. CANID SPECIALIST GROUP CONSERVATION OFFICER,
ALISON HOOD, OPERATION WOLF PROJECT MANAGER,
The Born Free Foundation

The Wolf Watchers

As the first rays of the dawn sun began to warm the chill night air of the Ethiopian Highlands, Kebero the young she-wolf yawned and stretched herself awake. As she looked around, she could see that most of her family had already started the day. This year's litter of young pups were busy filling themselves with warm milk from her mother Juno. Her father, Jupiter the pack leader, was exchanging morning greetings with the other wolves and the den was filled with the sounds of snuffling, squeaking and the swish of wagging tails.

Kebero shook the dust from her glossy red coat and joined in the morning ritual, grooming and being groomed by other wolves in equal measure. Jupiter began to howl and one by one the rest of the wolves joined in the chorus. With closed eyes, and muzzles pointed skywards, the strange choir voiced their eerie, beautiful wolf-song, announcing the start of a new day, just as they had for generation upon generation, down the long years of their history.

The wolves' song carried far on the still morning air, down into the valley and the tiny village far below the den. But the villagers did not look up in wonder at the sound of the ancient song, for many did not care for the wolves and all they stood for. They tolerated their presence in the mountains, but they were suspicious of them as a possible threat to their sheep and cattle. They did not understand their ways, their sense of family and their love for one another.

Back at the den, Kebero had stayed behind to look after the pups while the rest of the family went hunting. Like the other wolves, she loved to roam the wild plateau that surrounded their home, hunting for choice morsels to bring back for her family to share. But she also looked forward to puppy-sitting her younger brothers and sisters.

Next year she would be old enough to raise her own litter, but for now she was content to watch her siblings play - staging mock fights, pouncing on unsuspecting insects, running, jumping and rolling in the dust until they were exhausted. This play was essential for their development, helping to strengthen their muscles and tune their senses as they learnt how to become adult wolves.

The Wolf Watchers

The pups were too young to be alert to danger, but not Kebero. Always she remained constantly watchful, alert to any threat. So when the great tawny eagle wheeled silently across the sky, she was ready - pushing the pups into the safety of the cave. Standing at the entrance, Kebero remained tense - for besides the eagle she could sense another presence on the otherwise deserted plateau.

The Wolf Watchers

Far away, on a distant ridge, Kebero finally spotted three figures on horseback. Her body stiffened at first and then relaxed, for she had seen these people before. At first she had been afraid, for seldom did humans mean well when it came to wolves. But over many months she had learned that the strangers meant no harm. If anything they were a nuisance, these wolf-watchers who seemed to have nothing better to do than stare at Kebero and her family.

As the sound of their voices drifted across the plateau towards her, Kebero turned back to watching the pups, the moment of danger passed. But if only Kebero had been able to understand the humans' strange language, she would have soon realised that a far greater danger than the eagle lurked on the plateau, a danger that threatened not just her and her family, but all the wolves of Ethiopia...

The Wolf Watchers

The Wolf Watchers

From far away on the ridge the three scientists watched Kebero and the pups with concern in their eyes.

"It's great to see them so well and happy," said Claudio, "but I'm still worried. Too many other packs are falling ill."

"It's only a matter of time before the rabies spreads here, too," added his colleague Karen.

"Yes," replied the third party member Edriss sadly. "If we don't act soon it will be too late."

"Tomorrow we must meet with the village elders again," said Claudio. "Without their co-operation our plan to save the wolves will never work."

The wolf-watchers turned their horses round and left Kebero in peace. They knew all too well the danger that threatened the wolves' peaceful existence. Rabies, a devastating disease, had found its way from the villages into the wilderness of the mountains and the wolves had no defence against it. For centuries the wolves had lived in isolation on the plateau, but the arrival of domestic dogs used to herd the villagers' cattle had brought the killer disease into the very heart of their homeland.

As the wolf-watchers rode back to their camp over the open grassland, Juno, Jupiter and the rest of the pack were busy going about their daily routine, oblivious to the danger that lurked so close by.

The first task of every morning was to patrol the borders of their territory and re-mark the boundaries. The older pack members knew how important this was, but the less-patient younger ones began to desert the group to concentrate on the fun of hunting. Unlike their northern cousins the grey wolves, Ethiopian wolves hunt alone, for they are not after large animals that need to be run down by a co-ordinated pack. Instead, they prey on mole rats and grass rats, small creatures that need to be trapped by stealth and careful, patient searching.

The Wolf Watchers

Jupiter, as pack leader, knew better than anyone else where the best and fattest mole rats could be found. He could sniff out their burrows and then had the patience to wait for his prey to come to him. When the mole rat finally appeared out of its hole, Jupiter would freeze, leaning forward alert to every scent, sound and movement. Timing his attack to perfection, in a split second he would pounce, grabbing the plump meal in his mouth.

Today, Jupiter had made an early kill which pleased him,
but something else was making him feel uneasy.

Sensing danger, Jupiter dropped the prized mole rat and lifted his head to sniff the air. He knew the scent of a dog and that was what he could smell now. He had seen dogs with the cattle and villagers at the water hole, but always they had avoided each other. So what was one doing up here, far away from the cattle herds and the village, right in the heart of the wolves' hunting ground?

Jupiter was confused and nervous, tensing his muscles in readiness for an attack. He could see the dog now, trotting towards him across the grass, but something seemed wrong with it. It was limping and lop-sided and, even from a distance, Jupiter could see that it was shivering. Its eyes were terrible and red, staring not at him but somewhere in the distance. As Jupiter watched in bewilderment, the dog's tongue rolled from side to side and saliva frothed over its lips.

T he dog thrashed its head from side-to-side, growling and snapping at imaginary flies. Jupiter flattened himself against the ground and watched its every movement.

He was afraid for himself and his family for he had seen other dogs act this way, and other wolves, and he knew that this strange sickness eventually led to death. Suddenly, the dog arched its back and leapt at Jupiter, clawing at the empty air as the wolf rolled quickly aside. Jupiter had no intention of fighting this particular foe. Instead, his only thought was to lead the mad dog as far away from the den as possible, so he ran off in the opposite direction with the dog snapping at his heels. Farther and farther away from the den Jupiter ran, drawing the dog with him until it was staggering with exhaustion.

At last Jupiter left the dog behind, panting in the dust. Though shaken by his encounter, the wolf continued with his hunt for food — he knew he must take something back for Kebero and the cubs. After securing his third mole rat, Jupiter at last began the long walk back to the den.

Kebero was waiting impatiently for him to return. Minding the pups was a tiring business and she was hungry. As Jupiter came into sight, she knew that he would be bringing a tasty morsel and ran to greet him. The puppies followed eagerly. As each pack member returned to the den they were each greeted by the others in a similar fashion. Juno inspected her young pups and affectionately ran her tongue over their soft fur as they settled down to suckle.

Jupiter was glad to be back within the safety of the den. The encounter with the dog had been unsettling, even though he had come to no harm. Tucking his nose beneath his paws he settled down, along with all the other members of the pack, to sleep.

The Wolf Watchers

Back at their camp, Claudio and his team were collecting drugs and medical equipment ready to visit the village elders the following day. They knew that time was short if they were to save the wolves and they badly needed to persuade the people of the highlands to help them.

For many months they had been visiting village after village, explaining the danger of rabies and what it could mean for the wolves, explaining what needed to be done to prevent the disease spreading yet further through the countryside. But all too often the elders thought of wolves only as a nuisance rather than creatures that needed to be taken care of.

Gradually, though, Claudio and his team were helping to convince the people that something had to be done to save the wolves. They explained how they fed only on grass rats and mole rats not on sheep, keeping these small creatures under control so that *they* did not become a pest to the villagers. They explained how the wolves, like the other animals of the highlands, were part of the villagers' heritage, part of their native land and their history - a part that should be protected rather than destroyed.

And so the next day dawned and the wolf-watchers set off to resume their task, hoping that today they might have a chance to put their plan to save the wolves into action. When they entered the first village, they were greeted by the village elders and sat down to share beakers of hot, strong coffee.

Claudio explained again that the rabies was in danger of spreading. He asked them if they had not noticed what was happening to their own cattle dogs and could tell by their reaction that they too had witnessed the devastating effects of the disease. The elders listened intently as he explained that the only hope for the wolves, and the dogs, was for the disease to be attacked at source.

"We must vaccinate your cattle dogs," explained Claudio. "Then they will be safe from the disease and no longer capable of passing it on to the wolves." Once they had listened to what Claudio had to say, the elders talked for some time amongst themselves. At last, one spokesperson came forward.

"We agree to your plan," he said. "If you wish to start now, we will begin to round up our dogs." Claudio and his team were delighted - this was the breakthrough they had been waiting for for so long. Soon they had vaccinated all the dogs in the first village and were ready to move on - there was still much work to do.

As the days passed, the wolf-watchers moved from village to village, spreading the message and stopping the spread of the killer disease. High above them, amongst the peace of the mountains, Kebero woke and proudly looked around her family. Thanks to the wolf-watchers and their work, life for Jupiter and his pack would carry on as normal and Kebero could still look forward to mothering her own pups.

As their ritual morning howl echoed across the plateau, Claudio reflected on the fact that, for the time being at least, this particular pack of wolves were safe from at least one very real danger. There were other villages to visit and other wolves to save, and he knew all too well that the future of the Ethiopian wolf was still uncertain. So for now Claudio and his team would carry on watching, even if the wolves do think that they're just being nosey.

The Wolf Watchers

Dr Claudio Sillero-Zubiri inspects the wolves' stronghold in the highlands of Ethiopia

The Bale Mountains National Park - over 1,000 square kilometres of unspoilt wilderness where the Ethiopian wolf survives in relative safety.

The Ethiopian wolf is the world's most endangered species of dog. There are probably less than 400 of them left in the wild and those that remain face many threats - habitat loss, persecution by humans as well as the many dangers that domestic dogs can bring, particularly from disease.

Addendum

THE **REAL** STORY

"We will fail in our quest to conserve Nature if we do not protect the Earth's fragile ecosystems as a whole, but we would be poorer in spirit without the ability to mourn the death of an old wolf friend..."

Dr Claudio Sillero-Zubiri

The most lethal of these is rabies, a killer against which the wolves have little chance of survival. Here's how we helped to even up the odds - in the hope that the Ethiopian wolf will survive the growing threat of extinction.

High in the uplands of Ethiopia lie the Bale Mountains, last stronghold of the Ethiopian wolf and homeland to the Oromo highlanders, native peoples who have tended to their livestock on these hillsides for many hundreds of years.

Historically, wolves and humankind have lived side by side, each largely indifferent to the other, their paths seldom having cause to cross. Over the thousand square kilometres of the mountain range - grassy plateaux interspersed with steep, rocky slopes - there was room for everyone to live in peace. The small wolf population existed largely within the safety of the Bale Mountains National Park, an unspoilt wilderness, designated as a sanctuary for wildlife in 1970. But times were set to change...

1990-92

Following the overthrow of the Ethiopian government, mounting unrest in the countryside eventually led to many highlanders moving into the Park. Devastation followed. Driven by the need for new grazing areas for their cattle, they cut down trees, burned and cleared areas of heather and grassland, and shot and killed both wolves and other wildlife.

Luckily, Dr Claudio Sillero-Zubiri, world expert on the Ethiopian wolf and his research team were on hand to try and stem the damage.

Based at Oxford University and funded by, among others, the Born Free Foundation, they had been studying the

While the cubs learn essential skills through play, the adult wolves hunt for mole rats on the surrounding plateau.

Ethiopian wolf, tracking its dwindling population, since 1988 and had been involved in the day-to-day management of the National Park. In the face of this new threat, creating an understanding of

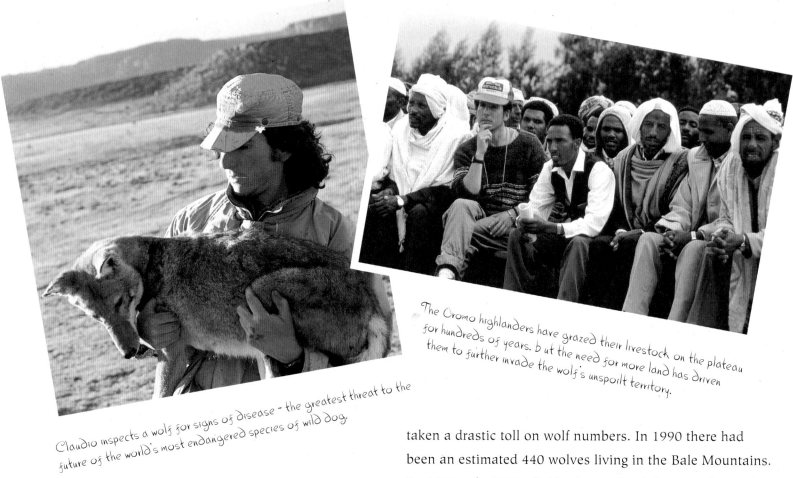

Claudio inspects a wolf for signs of disease - the greatest threat to the future of the world's most endangered species of wild dog.

The Oromo highlanders have grazed their livestock on the plateau for hundreds of years. but the need for more land has driven them to further invade the wolf's unspoilt territory.

the wolves and their needs became their top priority and, after lengthy discussions with the village elders, they finally managed to put an end to the shootings. They also began to put together an educational programme which, over time, would raise conservation awareness amongst the people of Ethiopia, helping them to protect their unique habitats and wildlife. But another danger lay just around the corner...

1992–1995

Over three years, the killer disease rabies swept like wildfire amongst the Ethiopian wolf population. Spread by the highlanders cattle dogs, who were now living in even closer proximity to the wolf packs, the outbreaks of rabies had taken a drastic toll on wolf numbers. In 1990 there had been an estimated 440 wolves living in the Bale Mountains. By 1995 only 150 individuals remained. It seemed now that disease was the single biggest threat to the wolves and their future. Claudio and his team recognised the need for an immediate vaccination programme to prevent further spread of both rabies and canine distemper, but first funding for such a venture had to be raised.

1996

By January 1996 sufficient money had been raised for the vaccination programme to start. First, agreement from the village elders was obtained and, after much discussion the cattle dogs in each area were rounded up for inspection and injection! So far, approximately 600 dogs have been treated - a figure which represents about 50% of the dogs living in

Action Plan for the Future

The work to safeguard the future of the Ethiopian wolf still goes on. Here's Claudio and his team's three-point plan for wolf survival:

The vaccination programme for local dogs needs to continue in order to stop the further spread of this lethal disease, helping the health of both the dogs and the wolves.

The Park and the wolves need protection! Regular patrols are needed to keep a close eye on the wolves and other wildlife.

The education programme needs to be maintained, providing leaflets, posters and school educational packs so that local people can learn about Ethiopian wildlife and develop an understanding that will help them live in harmony with their animal neighbours.

The highlanders dogs are the principle carriers of the lethal disease rabies. Introducing a regular innoculation programme (right) is Claudio's number one priority to ensure the health and safety of both wolves and the dogs themselves.

close proximity to the wolves. It is hoped that, by the time this book is published all relevant dogs will have given the necessary vaccine. However, Claudio and his team recognise that their job in helping to protect the wolves is far from over. For a start, the vaccine only lasts three years and will then need to be readministered if the threat of rabies is to be kept at bay.

Opposite, you can see an outline of the continuing work that needs to be undertaken on the wolves' behalf. With constant vigilance and adequate funding, we can hopefully ensure that in years to come there will still be wolves roaming freely in the highlands of Ethiopia.

Though the threat of extinction is still present, the Ethiopian wolf is growing in numbers and its future looks brighter than before.

Established in 1987, by *Born Free* actors
Bill Travers and Virginia McKenna, the *Born Free Foundation* has
become one of the United Kingdom's most active and widely-
recognised animal welfare and wildlife conservation charities.
The Foundation's objectives are to prevent the needless
suffering of wild animals and to conserve wildlife
in its natural habitat wherever possible.
The BFF projects span the world – Canada, America, Kenya,
Tanzania, Ethiopia, Scotland and Romania – as well as wherever
the abuse of captive wild animals is to be found.
The BFF provides a unique programme of direct care for animals
in need, be it a rescued lion, otter, or chimpanzee, an elephant
family, wolf family or orca family, responding and raising money to
help individual creatures as well as running long-term
conservation projects. We also hope to encourage a wider
understanding of the problems faced by many animal species.

You can directly help us by adopting an animal
and/or becoming a *Born Free* member.
Become part of the *Born Free* team and make things happen!
We can't do it without you!